LEARNING TOGETHER

ADVICE AND INSTRUCTIONS ON COMPLETING THESE TESTS

1.   There are 85 questions in each test. Make sure you have not missed a page.

2.   Start at question 1 and work your way to question 85.

3.   If you are unable to complete a question leave it and go to the next one.

4.   Do not think about the question you have just left as this wastes time.

5.   If you change an answer make sure the change is clear.

6.   Make sure you spell correctly.

7.   You may do any rough work on the test paper or on another piece of paper.

8.   Each test should take approximately 50 minutes.

9.   When you have finished each test mark it with an adult.

10. An adult may be able to explain any questions you do not understand.

TEST 16

SCORE _____

1. Which letter occurs twice in CRENELLATED but once in CREDENTIALS? (L)

2. Which letter occurs once in HARMONIOUS, once in LIBERATE but not at all in MELANCHOLY or in LIKE? (R)

3. Which letter, which occurs more than once, occurs as often in PRIVILEGED as it does in PROCEDURE? (E)

4. Half of a number is three quarters of 12. What is twice that number? ( )

5. Share 36 apples among Paul, Alan and Sam in such a way that for every 3 apples Paul gets, Sam gets 2, and Alan gets 4. How many apples does Alan get? ( )

In the questions below TWO words must change places so that the sentence makes sense. Underline the TWO words that must change places.

Look at this example: **The _wood_ was made of _table_.**

6. Their pupils sat quietly at the desks.

7. In sails fluttered gently the the breeze.

8. Some fins have spiky fish on their backs.

9. David was unable and sick to attend school.

10. Tropical cattle are being cleared to raise forests on the land.

The table below gives some information about the subtraction of numbers in the left-hand column from those in the top row.

Complete the table correctly using only the numbers given.

5.7,   4.9,   7.3,   7.1,   1.6

11. −	7.8		12.0
12, 13.	2.9	2.4	
14, 15.	6.2		10.4

In each question below one letter can be removed from the word in the first column and put into the word in the second column to give two new words. The order of the letters is not changed.
Look at this example:

| THINS | TOUT | (THIN) | (STOUT) |

16.	SHOUT	STOP	(_Shut_)	(_stoop_)
17.	THREAD	SOP	(_tread_)	(_Shop_)
18.	HEARD	SET	(_herd_)	(_seat_)
19.	BEAR	OUGHT	(_ear_)	(_bought_)
20.	SPORT	ANTS	(_spot_)	(_rant_)

In each line below write in the brackets one letter which completes the word in front of and the word after the brackets.

Look at this example: ROA (D) OOR

Here D completes ROAD and begins DOOR.

21.	MOS	(_S_)	IREN
22.	NEX	(_t_)	APER
23.	PYLO	(_N_)	AIL
24.	DEPRIV	(_E_)	URASIA
25.	INSER	(_t_)	AN

In each line below underline TWO words, ONE from each side, which together make ONE correctly spelt word. The word on the left always comes first. Look at this example:

| **BLACK** | ALL | TOP | AND | **BIRD** | BOY |

26.	ALL	_IN_	BY	SCORE	SCRIBE	PORT
27.	NO	IF	NOW	YES	ON	SO
28.	BY	AT	BUTTER	CYCLE	LOST	CUP
29.	SAT	UP	SO	BY	URN	GASP
30.	PATH	PASS	PART	OLD	PAT	AGE

Write in the brackets a word that rhymes with the second word and has a similar meaning to the first word.

Look at this example: SICK MILL (__ILL__)

31. AEROPLANE MET (Jet)

32. DOG SOUND (Lound)

33. DISCOVER LINED (Fined)

In a certain code CHRISTMAS is written as AFPGQRKYQ.
Write the following words in code. The alphabet is printed to help you.

A B C D E F G H I J K L M N O P Q R S T U V W X Y Z Code

34. BEFORE (ZCDMGP

35. DANGER (BYLOGP)

36. NAPKIN (LYNJGN)

What do these coded words represent?

37. EPMSN (Group)

38. CKCPEC (EMerge)

39. AYJASJYRC (calculate)

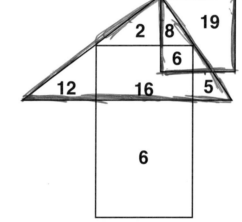

Questions 40-44 are about the above diagram which is made from a square, a rectangle and a triangle.

40. Which number is in all three shapes? (6)

41. From the sum of the numbers appearing only in the square, subtract the sum of the numbers appearing only in the triangle. (0)

42. What is the sum of all the numbers which appear in more than one shape? (30)

43. In how many shapes does the square root of 36 appear? (3)

44. Add the two highest even numbers and from the total subtract all the odd numbers. (4)

In the questions below 2 of the words in the brackets can be made from the letters of the word outside the brackets. Underline both words.

Look at this example:

CURTAIN   (**TRAIN**   CUSTARD   STAIN   **RAIN**   TRACK)

45. TEMPERATURE   (PAPER   RATE   AFTER   MATURE   MEANT)
46. BACKWARDS   (REWARD   DWARF   RACK   DRAW   SWORD)
47. LEARNING   (NEAR   BEARING   RING   REAP   PEARL)
48. YESTERDAY   (STEEP   DREAM   READ   STEER   PESTER)
49. CONSONANTS   (COUSINS   STAND   SOON   TENTS   TONS)
50. POTATOES   (STATE   PEAS   TOTAL   STOATS   GRATE)

In the questions below underline 2 words which are closest in meaning. Underline 1 word from each set of brackets.

Look at this example:

(**LITTLE**   WASP   BIN)   (INSERT   **SMALL**   RUBBISH)

51. (dig   hole   spade)   (pit   garden   fork)
52. (paper   pliers   plain)   (simple   pen   hammer)
53. (prize   money   lose)   (award   envelope   take)
54. (holiday   weekend   computer)   (days   game   vacation)
55. (ice   foam   laugh)   (lavish   froth   cold)

In questions 56-61 the three words A, B and C are in alphabetical order. The word at B is missing and you are given a dictionary definition instead. Write the correct word in the space.

Look at this example:

A) Flap
B) (__FLARE__) Distress signal from a boat.
C) FLASH

56.
(A) PREVAIL
(B) (PREVENT) To stop.
(C) PREY

57.
(A) DUST
(B) (DUTCH) Of Holland.
(C) DUTY

58.
(A) SCRAP
(B) (SCRATCH) Score with claws or nails.
(C) SCRAWL

59.
(A) MANNER
(B) (MANCE) Residence of a minister.
(C) MANUAL

60.
(A) RINSE
(B) (RIOT) Trouble caused by a crowd of people.
(C) RIP

61.
(A) AKIN
(B) (ALARM) Mechanical device to alert people.
(C) ALBINO

The words below and those in the lists are alike in some way. Write the letter of the list, that each word belongs to, in the brackets. Each letter may be used only once.

62. MAJESTIC (D)

63. GAGGLE (B)

64. PYRENEES (C)

65. FORTH (A)

66. LIME (E)

A.	B.	C.	D.	E.
MERSEY	SHOAL	ANDES	ELEGANT	BEECH
TYNE	FLOCK	ROCKIES	STATELY	BIRCH
THAMES	LITTER	ALPS	GRACEFUL	OAK

Complete these sequences, the alphabet is printed to help you.

A B C D E F G H I J K L M N O P Q R S T U V W X Y Z

67. A, C, G, M   (U)

68. C, Y, F, V, I   −4, +7   (S)

69. ZYY, ABB, YXX, BCC, XWW   (DDD)

70. ZY, UT, RQ, ML, JI   (ED)

```
                1
                X

        4   3   2
        X   X   X

        5   6
        X   X
```

A, B, C, D, E and F are six towns at the points 1-6 but not in that order.
A is due north of C which is due east of B.
B is due south of F which is one of the two most westerly towns.
E is not furthest north.

71. Which town is at point number 1?   (D)

72. Which town is at point number 2?   (E)

73. Which town is at point number 3?   (A)

74. Which town is at point number 4?   (F)

75. Which town is at point number 5?   (B)

76. Which town is at point number 6?   (C)

A certain month has 5 Wednesdays and the 6th of the month is a Sunday.

77. What date is the third Thursday of the month?   (17th)

78. How many Saturdays are there in the month?   (4)

79. What day is the 26th of the month?   (Saturday)

80. How many Tuesdays are there in the month?   (5)

	Mon 3rd	Tues 4th	Wed 5th	Thurs 6th	Fri 7th	Sat 8th
CUBS	57	19	76	67	73	49
BROWNIES	29	35	56	66	37	58
SCOUTS	27	26	76	47	36	114

This table shows the number of Cubs, Brownies and Scouts who went to see Peter Pan in January 2000. The dates of the days are given.

81. On which day and date were there twice as many Scouts at Peter Pan as there were Cubs on Mon 3rd?   (_____)

82. On which day and date did most Brownies attend Peter Pan?   (_____)

83. On which day and date did the number of Brownies and Scouts added together equal the number of Cubs attending Peter Pan?   (_____)

84. On which day and date were there 27 less Cubs at Peter Pan than attended on Wed 5th?   (_____)

85. How many Brownies attended Peter Pan throughout the whole week? (_____)

TEST 17

SCORE _____

1. Which letter occurs once in MARBLE but twice in CONCRETE? (_____)

2. Which letter occurs twice in RECTANGLE but only once in TRIANGLE? (_____)

3. Which letter occurs three times in PARALLELOGRAM and three times in QUADRILATERAL? (_____)

4. Half of a number added to 8 is 7 less than 28. What is the number? (_____)

5. A pencil costs twice as much as a rubber. Two pencils and a rubber cost 50p. How much is a rubber? (_____)

In the questions below TWO words must change places so that the sentence makes sense. Underline the TWO words that must change places.

Look at this example: **The <u>wood</u> was made of <u>table</u>.**

6. Start at the end and finish at the beginning.

7. Learning is the key to reading.

8. Was money the locked in the drawer?

9. The racing car burst on flames into impact.

10. Only computers make mistakes, not humans.

The table below gives some information about the addition of numbers in the top row to those in the left-hand column.
Complete the table correctly using only the numbers given.

3.0,   7.6,   1.0,   11.6,   4.1

	+	7.5	5.6	
11.				
12, 13.			9.7	5.1
14, 15.	2.0	9.5		

TEST 17 PAGE 1

In the questions below one word can be put in front of the other
words to form four new words. Write the correct word in the brackets.
Look at this example:

FLY	PROOF	WORKS	MAN	(FIRE)

16. LOW   LONG   SIDE   HIND   (_____)

17. DOG   DOZE   FROG   FIGHT   (_____)

18. FIRE   WARDS   WASH   WATER   (_____)

19. LONG   ACHE   LIGHT   LINE   (_____)

20. WRIGHT   THING   ABLE   HOUSE   (_____)

In each question write in the brackets one letter which will complete
both the word in front of the brackets and the word after the brackets.

Look at this example: ROA (D) OOR.

21. SHOWE   (_____)   EED

22. HAL   (_____)   LAP

23. PART   (_____)   ARD

24. DUM   (_____)   ALM

25. GAUG   (_____)   RUPT

In each line below underline TWO words, ONE from each side, which together make ONE
correctly spelt word. The word on the left always comes first.

Look at this example:

BLACK	ALL	TOP	AND	**BIRD**	BOY
26. PULL	OUT	PUT	FLAP	LET	IN
27. MAN	LAST	NOW	AND	HELP	AGE
28. CAN	CAT	CAR	HIS	CASE	HIM
29. OUT	COT	SHE	TON	RED	IN
30. AT	ON	AS	VEST	TONE	TACK

In each question below one letter can be removed from the word in the first column and put into the word in the second column to give two new words. The order of the letters is not changed.

Look at this example:

THINS   **TOUT**   (THIN)   (STOUT)

31. LATHER   ATE   (_____)   (_____)

32. HARPY   EAST   (_____)   (_____)

33. MINCE   KIT   (_____)   (_____)

34. FRILL   CHAT   (_____)   (_____)

35. POINT   HARD   (_____)   (_____)

Underline 2 words, one from each set of brackets, that have the same connection and will complete the sentence.

Look at this example:

UP is to (<u>DOWN</u> OVER LEFT)   as **COME is to (START <u>GO</u> AFTER)**

36. CLEAN is to (WASH SOAP DIRTY)   as HEAVY is to (LIGHT COAL LIFT)

37. FAST is to (WIN SLOW RUN)   as FACT is to (BOOK SENTENCE FICTION)

38. WHALE is to (FISH TROUT MAMMAL)   as TOAD is to (FROG RIVER AMPHIBIAN)

39. AEROPLANE is to (AIRPORT LAND ARRIVE)   as BOAT is to (WATER DOCK ANCHOR)

40. COW is to (CALF GRASS BULL)   as SOW is to (BOAR PORK GRUNT)

In the questions below one word, in bold print, has had three letters removed. These letters make a word. Write the words in the brackets.

Look at this example: We had tea in the TING Room   (SIT) The word is SITTING.

41. The race is **STING** at 1.00 o'clock.   (_____)

42. A wooden cross **MED** the grave.   (_____)

43. We were told to **INM** the police of any activity.   (_____)

44. In mathematics there are many 2 dimensional **SHS**.   (_____)

45. A **SE** is a useful garden tool for turning over soil.   (_____)

In the paragraph below five words are missing. Choose the most appropriate words from the lists below. One word from list A fills the space at A, one word from list B fills the space at B and so on.

<u>Underline the word you choose.</u>

The (**A**) entered his warm (**B**) where he has been carefully tending his young flowers. He was (**C**) to find that his assistant had failed to give the flowers (**D**) and that the loose soil was very (**E**).

46. A	47.B.	48.C.	49.D.	50.E.
PLUMBER	HALL	HAPPY	WATER	WET
FARMER	SITTING ROOM	ANNOYED	FOOD	HARD
FLORIST	HUT	LAUGHING	GRASS	COLD
DOCTOR	GREEN HOUSE	SMILING	SOIL	DAMP
JOINER	CAR	CHEERFUL	SNOW	DRY

In each question 51-56 the numbers in the second column are formed from the numbers in the first column by using a certain rule. Put the correct answer opposite the arrow. A different rule is used in each question.

51. 3.5 ⟶ 6
6.5 ⟶ 12
7.0 ⟶ 13
9.5 ⟶

52. 36 ⟶ 11
100 ⟶ 15
144 ⟶ 17
9 ⟶

53. 3 ⟶ 4.5
6 ⟶ 9.0
9 ⟶ 13.5
15 ⟶

54. 5 ⟶ 20
7 ⟶ 24
8 ⟶ 26
9 ⟶

55. 3 ⟶ 3.5
4 ⟶ 4.0
5 ⟶ 4.5
10 ⟶

56. 15 ⟶ 1
21 ⟶ 3
12 ⟶ 0
27 ⟶

Write in the brackets a word that rhymes with the second word and has a similar meaning to the first word.

Look at this example: SICK   MILL   (_ILL_)

57. INTERVAL   HULL   (_____)

58. UNIT   BUN   (_____)

59. STOP   FAULT   (_____)

60. BLAME   FUSE   (_____)

61. CARTON   FOX   (_____)

62. RUBBISH   TASTE   (_____)

Complete the sequences by inserting the correct numbers in the brackets.

63. 16, 24, 20, 28, 24   (_____)

64. 4.9, 6.1, 7.5, 9.1   (_____)

65. 80, 85, 95, 110, 130   (_____)

66. 625, 636, 647, 658   (_____)

67. 740, 739, 735, 726   (_____)

68. 39, 39, 34, 43, 29, 47   (_____)

69. A right-angled triangle has sides of 4cm and 8cms which touch to form a right-angle. What is half of its area?   (_____)

70. A circle can be drawn inside a square so that the circle just touches all four sides of the square. If the square has an area of 25 sq. cms. what is the radius of the circle?   (_____)

These questions are about the following shapes.

REGULAR PENTAGON,   **SQUARE,**
RIGHT-ANGLED TRIANGLE,   **RECTANGLE.**

Use this information only and answer these questions

71. Which shape or shapes do not have all internal angles the same?   (_____)

72. Which shape has most sides?   (_____)

73. Which shape or shapes could not be cut into 2 right-angled triangles using only one cut?   (_____)

74. Which shape or shapes could you not be sure would have at least one line of symmetry?   (_____)

Questions 75 - 78 are about the lines drawn inside the squares.

A	B	C	D	E

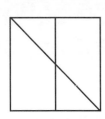 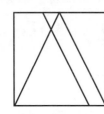 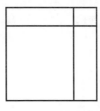 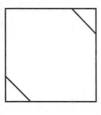 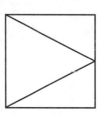

75. Name one square which has lines crossing at 45 degrees.   (_____)

76,77. Name two squares with parallel lines.   (_____) & (_____)

78. Name the square in which lines cross at right-angles.   (_____)

In the questions that follow letters replace numbers.
Calculate the sums and put the correct letters in the brackets.

Look at this example:

A = 2 B = 3 C = 4 D = 8 E = 12   D x A - C =   Letter __E__

79. A = 6 B = 3 C = 4 D = 1 E = 2   (C x D) – (C – B) = Letter ____

80. A = 6 B = 2 C = 12 D = 10 E = 5   (D – E) x (C - D) = Letter ____

81. A = 6 B = 4 C = 8 D = 7 E = 5   (C ÷ B) + (D – E) = Letter ____

82. A = 59 B = 3 C = 6 D = 2 E = 42   D x (C - B) =   Letter ____

In the questions below the words in brackets are formed from the 2 words outside the brackets.

Write the missing word in the brackets.

Look at this example:

CAT	(TO)	OUR		RING	(GO)		OVER
83. LIMP	(LINK)	SINK		BOWL	(	)	SEAT
84. SNAKE	(MAKE)	SMALL		HATS	(	)	SEAL
85. WHALE	(ABLE)	BARE		CHILDREN	(	)	MORE

TEST 18

SCORE _____

1. Which letter occurs as often in BEGINNING as it does in GRABBING? (___G___)

2. Which letter appears once in UNDERSTANDING, twice in PERMISSION but not all in THOUSANDS? (___I___)

3. Which letter occurs half as many times in REASONED as it does in GOVERNMENT? (___N___)

4. One third of a certain number is the same as one quarter of 60. What is the number? (___45___)

If Tim had 6p more he would have half as much as Jill.
Jill has 3 times as much as Fred who is 12p short of 30p.
How much does each one have?

5. Tim. (___21p___)

6. Jill. (___54p___)

7. Fred. (___18p___)

In the sentences below 2 words must change places to make the sentences sensible. Underline the TWO words. An example is shown.

The <u>wood</u> is made of <u>table</u>.

8. This time <u>Elizabeth</u> week <u>next</u> will be twelve.

9. The smoking <u>of</u> was in need <u>chimney</u> cleaning.

10. <u>Broke</u> the storm the clouds <u>after</u> up.

11. Cars <u>park</u> unable to <u>were</u> in the busy street.

12. Two boys <u>number</u> their coats on peg <u>hung</u> ten.

13. Slowly <u>sailed</u> ship <u>the</u> silently into port.

The table below gives some information about the addition of numbers in the left-hand column to numbers in the top row. Complete the table.

	+		5.5	7.6
15,16,17.	11.9			
18, 19.	8.7	17.4		

(14.)

In each question write in the brackets one letter which will complete both the word in front of the brackets and the word after the brackets.

Here is an example: ROA (D) OOR

20. HUL (____) ERB   21. DIA (____) OAN

22. FAD (____) STATE   23. LAS (____) OME

24. TO (____) RACE   25. WAR (____) USK

In each line below a word from the left-hand group joins one from the right-hand group to make a new word. The left-hand word comes first. Underline the chosen words. An example has been done to help you.

CORN	<u>FARM</u>	TIME		OVER	FIELD	<u>YARD</u>
26. PANE	SNAP	SET		LAST	MAD	PING
27. BAR	ON	FARE		SON	GAIN	WORD
28. HEAD	OVER	FOR		TURN	ROW	DRAWER
29. PALM	FOE	OUT		THUS	LET	TIN
30. MAIN	FALL	HAS		BODY	IT	LAND
31. EVER	INN	LET		SIDE	TING	YEAR

In the following questions a letter can be taken from the first word and put into the second word to form TWO new words. Write both NEW words.

Look at this example: THEN   TANK   (TEN)   (THANK)

The H moves from THEN to TANK and makes the new words TEN and THANK.

32. DICE   PATH   (_____) (_____)

33. STREAM   CAT   (_____) (_____)

34. FLAIR   HAVE   (_____) (_____)

35. PAINT   BAT   (_____) (_____)

36. GANG   LACE   (_____) (_____)

37. TAMPER   SANK   (_____) (_____)

The letters of the word in capitals have been jumbled up. Use the clue to unjumble the letters and write the correct word in the brackets.

Look at this example: KBOO - Contains stories   (BOOK)

38. ALEYLV - A river will run in this.   (_____)

39. PENEELOV - You put a letter in this for posting.   (_____)

40. CAOTTRR - You might use this on a farm.   (_____)

41. OTBETL - A container for liquid.   (_____)

Groups of words are printed below. The groups A-F are made up of words which are similar in some way.

A	B	C	D	E	F
padre	spear	hull	post	roast	rope
minister	lance	rudder	stop	boil	string
priest	javelin	bridge	tops	fry	cord

Decide into which of the above groups the following words must fit.
Write the group letter in the brackets.

42. pots   (_____)   43. twine   (_____)

44. stew   (_____)   45. pastor   (_____)

46. pike   (_____)   47. keel   (_____)

In a code words are written as shown below.

ORIENTAL   becomes **ABCDEFGH**   **BUGGY**   becomes   **IJKKL**

Write the following words in code.

48. IGNORANT (CKEABGEF)   49. TANGERINE (FGEKDBCED)

Decode the following words.

50. DEGIHD (ENABLE)   51. KGCDFL (GAIETY)

52. GFFABEDL (ATTORNEY)   53. HGEKJGKD (LANGUAGE)

The information below is about 4 boys W, X, Y and Z and the drinks that they like.

W and X are the only two who like both milk and lemonade.
X and Z are the only two who like both lemonade and tea.
Y and W are the only two who like both fruit juice and coffee.

54. Which drink does W not like?   (tea)

55. Who likes coffee but not lemonade?   (Y)

56. Who likes lemonade, tea and milk?   (X)

57. Who likes lemonade but not tea?   (W)

58. Who likes coffee and fruit juice but not milk?   (Y)

59. Which drink is the most popular?   (lemonade)

In a month there were 4 Wednesdays. The 19th of the month was a Saturday.

60. What day was the 1st of the month?   (_____)

61. What date was the third Sunday?   (_____)

62. Which month could it be? (May, February or April)   (_____)

63. What date was the last Friday of the previous month?   (_____)

64. What day was the 20th of the previous month?   (_____)

Complete the following sequences. The alphabet is printed to help you.

A B C D E F G H I J K L M N O P Q R S T U V W X Y Z

65. A   Y   B   W   C   (_____)

66. B   E   G   J   L   (_____)

67. FL   MG   HN   OI   (_____)

68. CCX   VDD   EET   RFF   (_____)

69. BDC   EGF   HJI   KML   (_____)

70. ZRC   ESY   XTG   IUW   (_____)

In each of the following questions 3 words are in alphabetical order. The second word has not been written but its meaning is given. Decide what the second word should be each time and write it in the brackets. Each dash in the brackets represents a letter. An example is shown to help you.

CROSS

(<u>C</u> <u>R</u> <u>O</u> <u>W</u> <u>D</u>) a large group of people.

CRUEL

MIRROR

71. (_ _ _ _ _)   person who hoards money.

MITTEN

HASTY

72. (_ _ _ _ _ _ _) short, light axe.

HAUNT

ORANGE

73. (_ _ _ _ _)   path of a planet around the sun.

OSTRICH

STRONG

74. (_ _ _ _ _ _)   artist's work-room.

STUTTER

LANTERN

75. (_ _ _ _ _ _)   storage room for food.

LATCH

COMFORT

76. (_ _ _ _ _)   humorous, funny.

CONCEAL

Together Pete, Anne, Rose, Tom and Fred have £84.
Rose has £3 less than Pete who has £5 more than Fred.
Fred has £5 less than Anne.
Tom has £20 which is £2 more than Pete.

77. How much has Pete?   (_____)

78. How much has Anne?   (_____)

79. How much has Rose?   (_____)

80. How much has Fred?   (_____)

Using the numbers 2, 3, 4 and 6 ONCE ONLY in each question, fill in
the spaces in a way that will make the statements correct.
An example is shown to help you.

2 + 3 + 4 + 6 = 15.

81. (_____ + _____) ▬ (_____ ▬ _____)   =   3.

82. (_____ + _____ + _____) X _____   =   26.

83. (_____ + _____)   X   (_____ ▬_____)   =   8.

84. (_____ X _____)   ▬   (_____ ▬_____)   =   8.

85. (_____ ▬ _____)   +   (_____ X _____)   =   25.

TEST 19

SCORE _____

1. Which letter appears the same number of times in the words REMEMBER and ENFORCEMENT?   (_____)

2. Which letter is in the word PRESIDENT but not in the word DEPRESSION?   (_____)

3. Which letter occurs twice as often in PARTICULAR as it does in SECRETARY?   (_____)

4. Six times a number is four more than twice 19. What is the number?   (_____)

In three years Alan will be twice as old as Bob was last year. Colin, who will be 5 next year, is 2 years younger than Bob. How old is each boy?

5. Alan   (_____)

6. Bob   (_____)

7. Colin   (_____)

In the sentences below 2 words must change places to make the sentences sensible. Underline the TWO words. An example is shown.

The <u>wood</u> is made of <u>table</u>.

8. Tom's watch and one was a half minutes fast.

9. The aeroplane flew just above an ground.

10. The bay was in rough for fishing too.

11. I to not reach could the top shelf.

12. Always before food well chew swallowing it.

13. Peter hugged long his lost brother.

The table below gives some information about the addition of numbers in the left-hand column to numbers in the top row. Complete the table.

	+			
14,15.	+	8.7		
16,17.	12.6		26.4	
18,19.		18.1		20

TEST 19 PAGE 1.

In each question write in the brackets one letter which will complete both the word in front of the brackets and the word after the brackets.

Look at this example: ROA (D) OOR

20. CAME ( ) ENS   21. TAR ( ) ASK

22. GE   ( ) AID   23. SCA ( ) ACK

24. FAN   ( ) ABLE   25. TAL ( ) ALM

In each line below a word from the left-hand group joins one from the right-hand group to make a new word. The left-hand word comes first. Underline the chosen words. An example has been done to help you.

CORN	FARM	TIME	OVER	FIELD	YARD
26. AIM	OVER	OUT	RING	PUT	TEAR
27. BAND	OR	GET	IT	GILL	BUT
28. FOR	SUM	TO	WORK	LET	WING
29. OVER	DEAD	COME	SON	LOCK	LEE
30. BE	SET	RAN	LESS	PANT	SACK
31. PORT	CORD	NO	ABLE	TAIL	HEAD

In the following questions a letter can be taken from the first word and put into the second word to form TWO new words. Write both NEW words.

Example: THEN   TANK   (TEN)   (THANK)

The H moves from THEN to TANK and makes the new words TEN and THANK.

32. NIECE   PACE   (_____) (_____)

33. BARON   NOSE   (_____) (_____)

34. YEAR   EARL   (_____) (_____)

35. MANAGER   HAD   (_____) (_____)

36. GAUNT   BARE   (_____) (_____)

37. PART   GEM   (_____) (_____)

Two words inside the brackets have similar meanings to words outside the brackets. Underline the TWO words each time.

Look at this example:

HORSE PIG CAT (FALCON <u>MOUSE</u> TROUT <u>BADGER</u> SNAKE)

38. DISCUS JAVELIN HURDLES (SPORT MARATHON SPRINT RUGBY GAMES)

39. SETTEE BENCH STOOL (CUSHION CHAIR BED THRONE CABINET)

40. RICE OATS RYE (GROWN BARLEY FOOD SERIAL WHEAT)

41. CHEERFUL CONTENTED GLAD (ECSTATIC GLUM HAPPY SAD FEELINGS)

42. BAFFLING COMPLICATED CONFUSING (EASY SMART PUZZLING DIFFICULT PROBLEM)

43. PRUNE CLIP TRIM (CUT LOP GRASS HORSE GARDEN)

In the sentences below there are 6 words missing. From the lists A to F choose the <u>MOST SUITABLE</u> words to complete the sentences.

Choose a word from list A to fill space A, a word from list B to fill space B and so on. <u>Underline the chosen word in each group.</u>

The power went (**A**) and I was left in darkness. I felt my way to the drawer to find a (**B**). Groping in the (**C**) I struck a light and the room was filled with a (**D**) glow. Pulling back the curtain I saw the street lights were (**E**). The fault, I decided, must be in my (**F**).

44. A	45. B	46. C	47. D	48. E	49. F
out	torch	room	little	lit	room
away	match	shadows	shiny	shattered	switch
bang	bulb	dark	blinding	off	house
off	lamp	silence	faint	out	plugs
dim	fuse	hall	piercing	broken	bulbs

The table below shows the number of people in various age groups in four villages called Sulby, Picton, Marlow and Widford.

Age group A - Up to 18 years of age.
Age group B - From 19 to 60 years of age.
Age group C - Over 60 years of age.

Age Group	SULBY	PICTON	MARLOW	WIDFORD
A	550	400	120	420
B	700	530	400	530
C	270	310	320	310

50. Which age group A, B or C has the greatest number of people? (_____)

51. Which age group A, B or C has the smallest number of people? (_____)

52. Which village has more than half as many people in group A as in groups B and C together? (_____)

53. Which village has one third of its population in group A? (_____)

54. Which village has one quarter of its population in group C? (_____)

In the questions below give the next number in each series.

55. 2   5   11   23   (_____)

56. 8.8   7.2   5.6   4   (_____)

57. 80   63   48   35   (_____)

58. (4, 9)   (11, 23)   (18, 37)   (____,____)

59. (27, 3)   (21, 7)   (15, 11)   (____,____)

The two sets of numbers in each line go together in a similar way. Write the missing number each time.

Example: (7 ⟶ 14 ⟶ 16)   (9 ⟶ 18 ⟶ <u>20</u>)

(Double number and add 2)

60. (8 ⟶ 3 ⟶ 10)   (14 ⟶ 9 ⟶ _____)

61. (7 ⟶ 21 ⟶ 24)   (10 ⟶ 30 ⟶ _____)

62. (16 ⟶ 4 ⟶ 3)   (36 ⟶ 6 ⟶ _____)

63. (2 ⟶ 8 ⟶ 13)   (4 ⟶ 64 ⟶ _____)

64. (12 ⟶ 6 ⟶ 1)   (24 ⟶ 12 ⟶ _____)

65. (27 ⟶ 3 ⟶ 14)   (64 ⟶ 4 ⟶ _____)

In each of the following questions find a word which has a similar meaning to the left-hand word and rhymes with the right-hand word.

Look at this Example: TREMBLE   RIVER   (SHIVER)

SHIVER rhymes with RIVER and means TREMBLE.

66. MAIDEN   WHIRL   (_____)

67. RATION   FAIR   (_____)

68. FAITHFUL   CLUE   (_____)

69. CABLE   TYRE   (_____)

70. SHIP   NOTE   (_____)

71. CONSTRUCT   ACHE   (_____)

In the following questions the numbers in the second column are formed from the numbers in the first column by using the same rule. Put the correct answer in the brackets for each question.

72. 3 ⟶ 8
     7 ⟶ 16
     10 ⟶ 22

     20 ⟶ (___)

73. 12 ⟶ 1
     15 ⟶ 2
     24 ⟶ 5

     30 ⟶ (___)

74. 2 ⟶ 7
     3 ⟶ 26
     4 ⟶ 63

     5 ⟶ (___)

75. 4 ⟶ 6
     7 ⟶ 12
     11 ⟶ 20

     24 ⟶ (___)

76. 4 ⟶ 3
     14 ⟶ 8
     20 ⟶ 11

     30 ⟶ (___)

77. 2 ⟶ 5
     4 ⟶ 17
     7 ⟶ 50

     9 ⟶ (___)

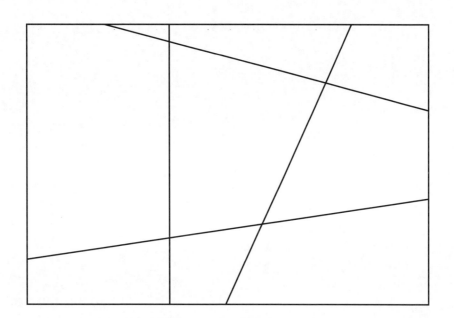

State whether the following statements about the diagram above are true or false. Write T for true or F for false in the brackets.

78. There are more than 6 right angles.   (_____)

79. There are more than 6 triangles.   (_____)

80. There are 3 lines parallel to one another.   (_____)

81. There are 3 horizontal lines.   (_____)

82. One of the lines divides the diagram into two
     equal pieces.   (_____)

Some letters from the word in capitals have been used to make other words. Underline the TWO words that have been made each time.

Look at this example:

CONVENIENT   <u>tonic</u>   video notion <u>voice</u>

83. COLLABORATE: barrel robot elated bear

84. DANDELION: dried   landed panda deal

85. MATHEMATICS: theme tame cheat thermal

TEST 20

SCORE _____

1. Which letter occurs as often in EPIDEMIC as it does in EPICURE and also occurs twice in DISCONNECT?   (_____)

2. Which letter, occurring once in GASTRONOMY, occurs twice in GASTRONOMIST and twice in GAZETTE?   (_____)

3. Which letter in GEANTICLINE occurs more than once and is closest to the end of the alphabet?   (_____)

4. When 6 is subtracted from a number it gives an answer which is 5 more than 29. What is the number?   (_____)

A cake costs 55p more than a packet of biscuits. Together they cost £2.05p.

5. How much is a cake?   (_____)

6. How much is a packet of biscuits?   (_____)

In the questions below TWO words must change places so that the sentence makes sense. Underline the TWO words that must change places.

Look at this example: The <u>wood</u> was made of <u>table</u>.

7. The neighbours that complained the music was too loud.

8. The was garage left open and unattended?

9. The sweet cake was laden with a beautiful trolley.

10. Three ambulances arrived within the minutes of the accident.

11. I could not the find word in my dictionary.

12. Air up are going fares next month.

The table below gives some information about the subtraction of numbers in the left-hand column from those in the top row. Complete the table correctly.

13.	-		3.9
14.		4.7	2.3
15.	2.9		1.0
16,17.		2.4	

In each line below write in the brackets one letter which completes the word in front of and the word after the brackets.

Look at this example: ROA (D) OOR

18. RHYTH   (_____)   URMUR

19. SLAN   (_____)   HEFT

20. SHEE   (_____)   INTH

21. STA   (_____)   OLK

22. POR   (_____)   LOPE

23. CUR   (_____)   AID

In each line below underline TWO words, ONE from each side, which together make ONE correctly spelt word. The word on the left always comes first.

Look at this example: <u>BLACK</u> ALL TOP   AND <u>BIRD</u> BOY

24.	AS	AFTER	AGO		GO	TASTE	MOON
25.	SEE	SAW	SAT		TED	DING	PAY
26.	NO	SERF	OF		VICE	ALL	PUT
27.	ARE	FEAT	CUT		HIM	BIT	HER
28.	HUM	OR	RIB		BUD	AN	GAIN
29.	COT	FLAT	PORT		TEN	END	TEND

In each question below, two consecutive letters can be removed from the word in the first column and put into the word in the second column to give two new words. The order of the letters is not changed and the two consecutive letters remain together.

Look at this example: **GIRD<u>LE</u>**   ASH   (GIRD) (<u>LE</u>ASH)

30.	HANDLE	BED	(_____)	(_____)
31.	CARPET	HELD	(_____)	(_____)
32.	BEDROOM	IT	(_____)	(_____)
33.	PILLOW	BELL	(_____)	(_____)
34.	FLOWER	BET	(_____)	(_____)

In questions 35-40 the three words A, B and C are in alphabetical order. The word at B is missing and you are given a dictionary definition instead. Write the correct word in the space.

Look at this example: A) FLAP
                                     B) (FLARE) Distress signal from a boat.
                                     C) FLASH

35. (A) NETTLE
     (B) (_ _ _ _ _ _ _) Not favouring either side.
     (C) NEVER

36. (A) BEVERAGE
     (B) (_ _ _ _ _ _) Be on one's guard.
     (C) BEWITCH

37. (A) SALAMANDER
     (B) (_ _ _ _ _ _) Fixed payment made to a person.
     (C) SALIVA

38. (A) THE
     (B) (_ _ _ _ _ _ _) A structure for showing drama.
     (C) THEIR

39. (A) PROSTRATE
     (B) (_ _ _ _ _ _ _) To guard from danger.
     (C) PROTEST

40. (A) STRIKE
     (B) (_ _ _ _ _ _) Fine cord.
     (C) STRIPE

The words below, and those in the lists, are alike in some way. Write the letter of the list that each word belongs to in the brackets. Each letter may be used only once.

A	B	C	D	E
FEZ	CROWD	QUAY	CUB	BAT
CROWN	RABBLE	DOCK	FOAL	FOX
BERET	GANG	HARBOUR	DUCKLING	HORSE

41. WHARF   (_____)

42. CYGNET   (_____)

43. TURBAN   (_____)

44. WHALE   (_____)

45. MOB   (_____)

In the following questions the letters of words have been jumbled up. A clue is given to help you each time.

Look at this example: **IATSDUM**   **Sports ground (Stadium)**

46. ALIEMDC   Examination by a doctor   (_____)

47. ODELUB   Twice the amount   (_____)

48. RAELCST   Brilliant orange-red colour   (_____)

49. UKARLEWM   Neither hot nor cold water   (_____)

50. ENALREG   High ranking army officer   (_____)

51. LEPTANEH   Hugh, thick skinned mammal   (_____)

Using the numbers 7, 8, 5 and 4 once only in each question fill in the spaces in any way which makes the statements correct.

52. (_____ + _____ + _____) - (_____) = 8

53. (_____ - _____) + (_____ - _____) = 6

54. _____ X (_____ + _____ + _____) = 80

55. (_____ X _____) - (_____ X _____) = 3

56. (_____ - _____) - (_____ - _____) = 0

57. (_____ + _____ - _____) X _____ = 24

A, B, C and D are four shops.
Only A and D are open late in the evenings and are closed on Sundays.
Only B and C have self-service and have a sale on at present.
Only D and B are closed on Sunday and have self-service.

58. Which shop is closed on Sunday and is not self-service? (___A___)

59. Which self-service shop has a sale but closes on Sunday? (___B___)

60. Which shop closes early and on Sunday? (___B___)

61. Which shop opens on Sunday and has a sale? (___C___)

62. Could you buy something in shop D late on a Sunday? (___No___)

63. Is there a self-service shop open late? (___No___)

	BREAM	ROACH	PIKE
ENGLAND	65	44	132
IRELAND	127.5	32.5	40
FRANCE	70	122.6	63.75

The above table shows the weight (in kgs.) of three different types of fish caught by three fishing teams in a fishing contest.

64. Which team caught half the weight in pike as Ireland caught in bream? (___France___)

65. Which team caught 3 times as much weight in pike as England caught in roach? (___England___)

66. Which team caught 1/5th of its total weight of fish in pike? (___Ireland___)

67. Which team's catch of bream was twice as heavy as Ireland's catch of roach? (___England___)

68. Which team caught 3/4's as much again in bream as Ireland caught in pike? (___France___)

Complete these sequences by inserting the correct letter(s) or number(s) in the brackets. The alphabet is printed to help you.

A B C D E F G H I J K L M N O P Q R S T U V W X Y Z

69. 121, 81, 49, 25   (___9___)

70. 104, 156, 208, 260   (___312___)

71. 4.70, 7.05, 9.40, 11.75   (___14.10___)

72. B, D, G, I   (___L___)

73. DBC, GEF, JHI, MKL   (___PNO___)

74. XBD, FCV, TDH, JER   (___PFL___)

Two words inside the brackets have similar meanings to the words outside the brackets. Underline the TWO words each time.

Look at this example: Horse, Pig, Cat   (falcon, <u>mouse</u>, snake, trout, <u>badger</u>)

75. Hammer   Saw   Screwdriver   (nail,   <u>spanner</u>,   <u>pliers</u>,   fork,   sharpener)

76. Tennis   Rugby   Football   (<u>golf</u>   badminton   archery   swimming   <u>netball</u>)

77. Kitten   Joey   Piglet   (bull   <u>tadpole</u>   boar   mare   <u>calf</u>)

78. Groom   Ring   Service   (home   curtain   <u>bride</u>   <u>bouquet</u>   garden)

79. Wool   Fur   Mink   (cotton   nylon   <u>silk</u>   <u>leather</u>   polyester)

80. Stockholm   London   Washington   (<u>Dublin</u>   Venice   Manchester   <u>Paris</u>   Glasgow)

In a certain code

DISCOUNT   is written as HMWGSYRX
JANUARY   is written as NERYEVC
MATCHES   is written as QEXGLIW

The alphabet is printed to help you.

A B C D E F G H I J K L M N O P Q R S T U V W X Y Z

What are these words in code?

81. POLISH   (___TSPMWL___)

82. SECRET   (___WIGVIX___)

83. TALKING   (___XEPOMRK___)

Decode these words.

84. IRKMRI   (___ENGINE___)

85. EYXLSV   (___AUTHOR___)

Answers to Test 16

1. L
2. R
3. E
4. 36
5. 16
6. THEIR — THE
7. IN — THE
8. FINS — FISH
9. UNABLE — SICK
10. CATTLE — FORESTS
11. 7.3
12. 4.9
13. 7.1
14. 1.6
15. 5.7
16. SHUT
17. TREAD — STOOP
18. HERD — SHOP
19. EAR — SEAT
20. SORT — BOUGHT
21. S — PANTS
22. T
23. N
24. E
25. T
26. IN — SCRIBE
27. NO — ON
28. BUTTER — CUP
29. SAT — URN
30. PASS — AGE
31. JET
32. HOUND
33. FIND
34. ZCDMPC
35. BYLECP
36. LYNIGL
37. GROUP
38. EMERGE
39. CALCULATE
40. 6
41. 0
42. 30
43. 3

44. 4
45. RATE — MATURE
46. RACK — DRAW
47. NEAR — RING
48. READ — STEER
49. SOON — TONS
50. STATE — PEAS
51. HOLE — PIT
52. PLAIN — SIMPLE
53. PRIZE — AWARD
54. HOLIDAY — VACATION
55. FOAM — FROTH
56. PREVENT
57. DUTCH
58. SCRATCH
59. MANSE
60. RIOT
61. ALARM
62. D
63. B
64. C
65. A
66. E
67. U
68. S
69. CDD
70. ED
71. D
72. E
73. A
74. F
75. B
76. C
77. 17TH
78. 4
79. SAT
80. 5
81. SAT 8TH
82. THURS 6TH
83. FRI 7TH
84. SAT 8TH
85. 281

* There may be other possible answers.

Answers to Test 17

1. E
2. E
3. A
4. 26
5. 10P
6. END — BEGINNING
7. LEARNING — READING
8. MONEY — THE
9. ON — INTO
10. COMPUTERS — HUMANS
11. 1.0
12. 4.1
13. 11.6
14. 7.6
15. 3.0
16. BE
17. BULL
18. BACK
19. HEAD
20. PLAY
21. R or D
22. F
23. Y
24. P or B
25. E
26. OUT — LET
27. MAN — AGE
28. CAR — CASE
29. COT — TON
30. AT — TACK
31. LATHE/LATER — RATE/HATE
32. HARP — YEAST
33. MICE — KNIT
34. FILL — CHART
35. PINT — HOARD
36. DIRTY — LIGHT
37. SLOW — FICTION
38. MAMMAL — AMPHIBIAN
39. AIRPORT — DOCK
40. BULL — BOAR
41. ART
42. ARK
43. FOR

44. APE
45. PAD
46. FLORIST
47. GREENHOUSE
48. ANNOYED
49. WATER
50. DRY
51. 18 (2 x − 1)
52. 8 (Square Root x + 5)
53. 22.5 (x + ½ x)
54. 28 (2 X + 10)
55. 7 (½ x + 2)
56. 5 (X ÷ 3) - 4
57. LULL
58. ONE
59. HALT
60. ACCUSE
61. BOX
62. WASTE
63. 32
64. 10.9
65. 155
66. 669
67. 710
68. 24
69. 8cm²
70. 2.5cm
71. RIGHT ANGLED TRIANGLE
72. REGULAR PENTAGON
73. REGULAR PENTAGON
74. RIGHT ANGLED TRIANGLE
75. A or B
76. B or D
77. B or D
78. C
79. B
80. D
81. B
82. C
83. BOAT
84. EATS
85. OMEN

These are the answers to Book 4 of a set of 4 graded books. A child who has not previously attempted questions of this type may have difficulty with the first few tests. However, research shows that a child's ability to handle and understand these questions generally increases with practice.

website: www.learningtogether.co.uk   E-mail: info@learningtogether.co.uk   Learning Together, 23 Carlston Avenue Holywood Co Down BT18 ONF Phone/Fax 028 9025852/028 90402086

Answers to Test 18

1. G
2. I
3. N
4. 45
5. 21P
6. 54P
7. 18P
8. ELIZABETH — NEXT
9. OF — CHIMNEY
10. BROKE — AFTER
11. PARK — WERE
12. NUMBER — HUNG
13. SAILED — THE
14. 8.7
15. 20.6
16. 17.4
17. 19.5
18. 14.2
19. 16.3
20. K
21. L
22. E or S
23. H or S
24. G or T
25. T or D or M
26. SNAP — PING
27. BAR — GAIN
28. OVER — TURN
29. OUT — LET
30. MAIN — LAND
31. LET — TING
32. DIE — PATCH
33. STEAM — CART
34. FAIR — HALVE
35. PANT — BAIT
36. GAG — PANT
37. TAMER — LANCE
38. VALLEY — SPANK
39. ENVELOPE
40. TRACTOR
41. BOTTLE
42. D
43. F
44. E
45. A
46. B
47. C
48. CKEABGEF
49. FGEKDBCED
50. ENABLE
51. GAIETY
52. ATTORNEY
53. LANGUAGE
54. TEA
55. Y
56. X
57. W
58. Y
59. LEMONADE
60. TUESDAY
61. 20TH
62. FEBRUARY
63. 28TH
64. THURSDAY
65. U
66. O
67. JP
68. GGP
69. NPO
70. VVK
71. MISER
72. HATCHET
73. ORBIT
74. STUDIO
75. LARDER
76. COMIC
77. 18
78. 18
79. 15
80. 13
81. (2 + 3) - (6 - 4) **
82. (4 + 6 + 3) x 2 **
83. (6 + 2) x 4 - 3) **
84. (3 x 4) - (6 - 2) **
85. (3 - 2) + (6 x 4) **

Answers to Test 19

1. E
2. T
3. A
4. 7
5. 7
6. 6
7. 4
8. AND — WAS
9. THE — AN
10. IN — TOO
11. TO — COULD
12. BEFORE — CHEW
13. LONG — HIS
14. 13.8
15. 10.6
16. 21.3
17. 23.2
18. 9.4
19. 23.2
20. L
21. L
22. M
23. R or B
24. G
25. C
26. OUT — PUT
27. BAND — IT
28. TO — WING
29. DEAD — LOCK
30. RAN — SACK
31. PORT — ABLE
32. NICE — PEACE
33. BARN — NOOSE
34. EAR — EARLY
35. MANAGE — HARD
36. AUNT — BARGE
37. PAT — GERM
38. MARATHON — SPRINT
39. CHAIR — THRONE
40. BARLEY — WHEAT
41. ECSTATIC — HAPPY
42. PUZZLING — DIFFICULT
43. CUT — LOP
44. OFF
45. MATCH
46. DARK
47. FAINT
48. LIT
49. HOUSE
50. B
51. C
52. SULBY
53. WIDFORD
54. PICTON
55. 47
56. 2.4
57. 24
58. 25, 51
59. 9, 15
60. 16 (X - 5 + 7)
61. 33 (3 X + 3)
62. 5 (Sq root X - 1)
63. 69 (X cubed + 5)
64. 7 (1/2 X - 5)
65. 15 (cubed root X + 11)
66. GIRL
67. SHARE
68. TRUE
69. WIRE
70. BOAT
71. MAKE
72. 42 (2X + 2)
73. 7 (X ÷ 3) - 3
74. 124 (X cubed - 1)
75. 46 (2 X - 2)
76. 16 (X ÷ 2) +1
77. 82 (X sq + 1)
78. T
79. F
80. T
81. F
82. F
83. ROBOT — BEAR
84. LANDED — DEAL
85. TAME — CHEAT

Answers to Test 20

1. C
2. T
3. N
4. 40
5. £1.30
6. 75P
7. THAT — COMPLAINED
8. THE — WAS
9. CAKE — TROLLEY
10. THREE — THE
11. THE — FIND
12. UP — FARE
13. 6.3
14. 1.6
15. 3.4
16. 3.9
17. 0.0
18. M
19. T
20. N
21. Y
22. E
23. L
24. AFTER — TASTE
25. SEE — DING
26. NO — VICE
27. FEAT — HER
28. HUM — AN
29. FLAT — TEN
30. HAND — BLEED
31. CART — HELPED
32. BROOM — EDIT
33. PILL — BELLOW
34. FLOW — BERET
35. NEUTRAL
36. BEWARE
37. SALARY
38. THEATRE
39. PROTECT
40. STRING
41. C
42. D
43. A
44. E
45. B
46. MEDICAL
47. DOUBLE
48. SCARLET
49. LUKEWARM
50. GENERAL
51. ELEPHANT
52. (7+5+4) - 8 **
53. (7-4) + (8-5) **
54. 3 x (4+5+6) **
55. (7x5) - (4x8) **
56. (8-7) - (5-4) **
57. (8+5 - 7) x 4 **
58. A
59. B
60. B
61. C
62. NO
63. YES
64. FRANCE
65. ENGLAND
66. IRELAND
67. ENGLAND
68. FRANCE
69. 9
70. 14.10
71. 312
72. L
73. PNO
74. PFL
75. SPANNER — PLIERS
76. GOLF — NETBALL
77. TADPOLE — CALF
78. BRIDE — BOUQUET
79. SILK — LEATHER
80. DUBLIN — PARIS
81. TSPMWL
82. WIGVIX
83. XEPOMRK
84. ENGINE
85. AUTHOR

** Other answers may be correct.